Annual 2010

Welcome to 3rd & Bird!

We've got the best branches
and the best birds. It's the place to be!

Mr Beakman has a treasure hunt for you and Muffin.
Can you find 5 friendly worms and 5 friendly
ladybirds in your book?

If you need any help, dance along
to page 62 for the answers.

BBC CHILDREN'S BOOKS
Published by the Penguin Group
Penguin Books Ltd, 80 Strand, London WC2R 0RL, England
Penguin Group (USA) Inc., 375 Hudson Street, New York, New York 10014, USA
Penguin Group (Australia), 250 Camberwell Road, Camberwell, Victoria 3124, Australia
(a division of Pearson Australia Group Pty Ltd)
Canada, India, New Zealand, South Africa
Published by BBC Children's Character Books, 2009
10 9 8 7 6 5 4 3 2 1

www.3rdandbird.co.uk
ISBN 13: 978 1 405 90611 1
Printed in China

Contents

3rd & Bird

Introducing... all your birdie friends

Mr and Mrs Lovebird
(they're Muffin and Samuel's Dad and Mum)

Mrs Billingsley
(she loves gardening)

Quinn
(he's great at building things)

Muffin
(she's the youngest birdie on 3rd & Bird)

from 3rd & Bird!

Mr Beakman
(he's the teacher on 3rd & Bird)

Samuel
(he's Muffin's older birdie brother)

Missy
(she thinks she's perfect, which is sometimes perfectly annoying!)

Rudy
(she's Samuel's best friend)

Whose house?

Read the clues about where the birdies live, then follow the dotted line with your finger or a pencil to join them to their home.

The Lovebirds live in a home with a bright red roof.

Mrs Billingsley lives in a home that has a tower on the side of it.

Rudy lives in a home with wheels.
Quinn lives in a home with windmill sails on it.
Missy lives in a home that looks like a fruit.
Mr Beakman lives in a home with a blue door.

Helping out

On 3rd & Bird everyone has good ideas about what helping out is about!

Mum and Dad are always helping me - ever since I was just an egg, actually.

Mrs Billingsley loses things - all the time - which means she needs lots of help finding them. Rudy and Muffin and I love treasure hunts, so that's OK!

Quinn can mend just about anything. He's always fixing things around 3rd & Bird and coming up with great ideas for inventions that help us.

Mr Beakman is our teacher, so he helps us to learn about maths and writing and bird stuff like nest building, worm finding, and which way is north, south, east and west. Mr Beakman loves to sing, so he also teaches us wonderful tunes to whistle. And the great thing about Mr Beakman is that when things go wrong (which they sometimes do) he says:

"There's always a way!"

And there always is! Take the time when Muffin was learning to fly...

Muffin kept trying
Now Muffin is flying!

Stick a photo here, or draw a picture, of someone who helps you.

How do you like to help?

Make a Missy!

Here's how to create a collage picture of Missy

You will need:

- craft materials such as beads, sequins, feathers, stickers, buttons, ribbon
- scraps of material or coloured paper
- dried orange peel if you have it
- glue
- a grown-up to help you

1.
Ask an adult to help you trace the picture of Missy onto a sheet of paper.

2.
Stick on scraps of blue and yellow material or paper for Missy's body. Overlap the pieces to make the feathers.

3.
Add two bird feet in strips of orange paper or material. Or use dried orange peel - it looks great.

4.
Stick on a pointed beak in orange paper, material or orange peel.

5.
Give Missy a bright blue eye.

6.
Add a feather on top of her head. Or try colouring a feather with blue crayons.

7.
Missy likes dressing up, so you might want to put a necklace on her made from beads, buttons or stickers.

Show time!

Shake-a-shake da Muffin!

Da Muffin!

SING SAMUEL ....

DANCE RUDY ....

FLY MUFFIN ....

Dance, sing and dress up!

It's time to put on a show! Ask some of your friends or family to make up a dance with you, to one of your favourite songs. To make your show more colourful and fun, why not find all your dressing-up clothes and get everyone to choose their favourite costume.

Once you're dressed up, think about what your character will say and how they will move in the show.

For example, when Mr Beakman dressed up as the captain of a ship, he gave everyone orders and whistled very loudly!

Dot-to-dot

What have Samuel and Muffin drawn on Mr Beakman's board? Join the dots to find out.

1 2 3 4 5 6 7 8 9 10 11 12 13 14 15 16 17 18 19 20

Now colour your picture!

How many flowers?

Look at
Mrs Billingsley's
beautiful blooms!

Can you find:
one purple flower
two red flowers
three blue flowers
and four yellow flowers?

Finish the picture in your
favourite colours.

Race round 3rd & Bird!

Rudy, Muffin and Samuel are racing to the Bird Theatre. Who takes the quickest route and arrives first? Find out by tracing along the coloured string with your finger.

What do you think is happening at the Bird Theatre today? There's lots of singing and dancing! Why not join in.

Answer: Muffin arrives first.

Get creative!

Here's Rudy
dancing around at home.
Make the picture really colourful.

What colours did you use
for Rudy's curtains?

Who's who?

Look carefully at the shapes of Mr Beakman, Quinn, Rudy and Muffin.

Draw a line to match each shadow with their name.

Mr Beakman **Rudy**

Quinn **Muffin**

a

b

c

d

Answers: a Mr Beakman; b Rudy; c Muffin; d Quinn.

Dancing feet!

Anytime's a good time for dancing.

Mr Beakman's music is making everyone feel like dancing. Can you find the little pictures in the big picture?

Why don't you get on your feet!

Time for School!

Ding! Ding!
The school bell is ringing.
Mr Beakman is ready to start the lessons.
But where are Samuel, Muffin and Rudy?

Brighten up the school-house using your best colours.

Mystery parcels

Samuel is playing a game with Rudy. He has wrapped up some things for a guessing game.

What do you think is inside each parcel?

a

b

c

d

Answers: a) a ball; b) a shaker; c) a toy rocking horse; d) a toy elephant.

Shooting Stars!

Muffin was allowed to stay up late to see the stars shooting across the night sky.

Can you spot five differences between the top and bottom pictures?

Answers: Muffin has disappeared; a shooting star has appeared; the toy has disappeared from the cart; the pink flowers have disappeared; another yellow flower has appeared next to Missy.

Night flight

Samuel and Rudy are
having a night-time adventure.
Trace over the dotted lines of
the stars and colour the sky in

THE MUFFIN EXPRESS!

1 It was a lovely sunny day on 3rd & Bird. Mr Beakman was whistling a happy tune as he built a new train track, along a branch of the tree.

2 Samuel, Rudy and Muffin came to see what he was doing. They were impressed. They all loved trains. 'Choo! Choo!' cried Muffin.

'Choo indeed,' said Mr Beakman, who was feeling worried. 'The first train ride is today, at sunset. The track isn't finished, and I don't know where I put my conductor's hat.'

3 'We'll help you Mr B!' said the young birds. Singing and banging and hammering away, they worked hard on the train track, so that it would be finished by sunset.

4 But something went wrong with the bit of the track that Muffin built. It was all wobbly, and the train couldn't travel along it!

Rudy went to get Quinn to help them. 'We don't know how to fix this track,' explained Rudy. 'It's gone all wobbly!'

5 'There's nothing that clacks or clicks that your old pal Quinn can't fix,' Quinn reassured Rudy. 'Come on, young hatchlings, let's get to work!'

6 Singing and banging and hammering away, Samuel, Rudy and Quinn worked hard on the train track to finish it in time for the first ride at sunset.

7 When Mr Beakman flew in wearing his conductor's hat later that day, he was very impressed by all their work. 'It's looking splendid! Oh, thank you - just in time for sunset.'

8 Now it was time for Mr Beakman to climb into the conductor's seat, so that he could drive the train for the first ride. But he didn't fit. He was too big! Oh no! Who could drive the train now?

9 'Sounds like a duty for Rudy!' cried Rudy, but she couldn't squeeze into the seat either. 'There must be someone who can fit,' cried Rudy.

10 'Let me try!' said Samuel as he jumped in head first. 'It's quite dark in here,' he mumbled, before they pulled him out. Muffin sat watching from the branch above.

11 If no-one could drive the train, it would not run at sunset.

'We can't give up now,' said Mr Beakman, 'there is always a way!' So everyone whistled a happy tune while they tried to think of a plan.

12 As they were whistling, Muffin slipped down from the branch she was sitting on and dropped straight into the conductor's seat. 'Muffin fit!' she cried.

'Bird's the word!' said Samuel. 'You do fit!'

13 Mr Beakman gave Muffin the blue conductor's hat. 'Come on, everybirdy, all board!'

Muffin blew the whistle and the Muffin Express started to move slowly down the track.

14 'Puff! Puff! Toot! Toot! Choo! Choo!' called Muffin to Missy as they passed her house. Missy smiled and waved.

15 The Muffin Express (and everybirdy on board) whistled as they chugged along the branches of their tree and the sun set over 3rd & Bird.

The end

Toot! Toot!
Muffin is driving
the train.

Dress-up time!

'Oh, little birds!'
It's Missy calling, and she wants Muffin, Samuel and Rudy to play dress-up.
'Muffin play!' said Muffin, so they did.

Missy
likes being a fairy princess.

Muffin
likes fluttering like a butterfly.

Read the clues and choose the perfect costume for Missy, Samuel, Rudy and Muffin.

Draw a line from each costume to the correct bird.

Rudy
likes playing at farmers.
Samuel
likes sailing the high seas.

Make a match

Look carefully at the shadows. Can you draw a line using your finger to match the shapes to the coloured pictures?

1

2

3

4

a

b

c

d

Answers: 1b; 2c; 3d; 4a.

Dancing lessons

Mr Beakman is teaching Samuel a new dance. Colour the picture in your very best colours.

Can you do the Toucan Twist? Why don't you try it?

Muffin helps

Muffin wants to help Quinn make something.

But first they need all of Quinn's tools.

Help Muffin find:
eight cogs
three bolts
three nuts
one hammer

Imagine something that Quinn has made, with a little help from his friends.

Draw a picture of it here and write its name.

Quinn has made a ....

Dot-to-dot teatime

What's for tea on 3rd & Bird? Join the dots to find out.

Then colour the pictures.

a

1 2 3 4 5 6 7 8

b

1 2 3 4 5 6 7 8

c

1 2 3 4 5 6 7 8

Answers: a plum; b strawberry; c melon.

Fruity puzzle

Try and fill in the missing letters.

__elon

gra__es

__trawberry

plu__

Which is your favourite fruit? Draw a picture of it here.

Answers: melon; grapes; strawberry; plum.

Cute little Muffin

Samuel has just put this picture of his little sister Muffin, in a picture frame. Doesn't she look cute! Decorate the frame by following the colour code.

1 2 3 4

MUFFIN

Picture fun!

Why don't you make your own frame?

You will need:

- photo or other picture
- 2 pieces of plain card that are between 4 cm and 6 cm bigger all round than the picture
- pencil
- craft materials such as beads, sequins, feathers, stickers
- a grown-up to help you

1. Choose a favourite photo or picture of someone you like.

2. Ask a grown-up to place the picture in the middle of one of the pieces of card and trace lightly with a pencil round it so you can see where the outline is. Get the grown-up to cut around this outline to make the frame.

3. Now decorate the frame - try stickers, scraps of material or feathers. You might want to make it sparkle with sequins or foil.

4. Stick the picture in the middle of the other piece of card and then stick the frame over this.

It's framed!

Find the toys

Help Muffin to find six lost toys. Tick each box as you find them.

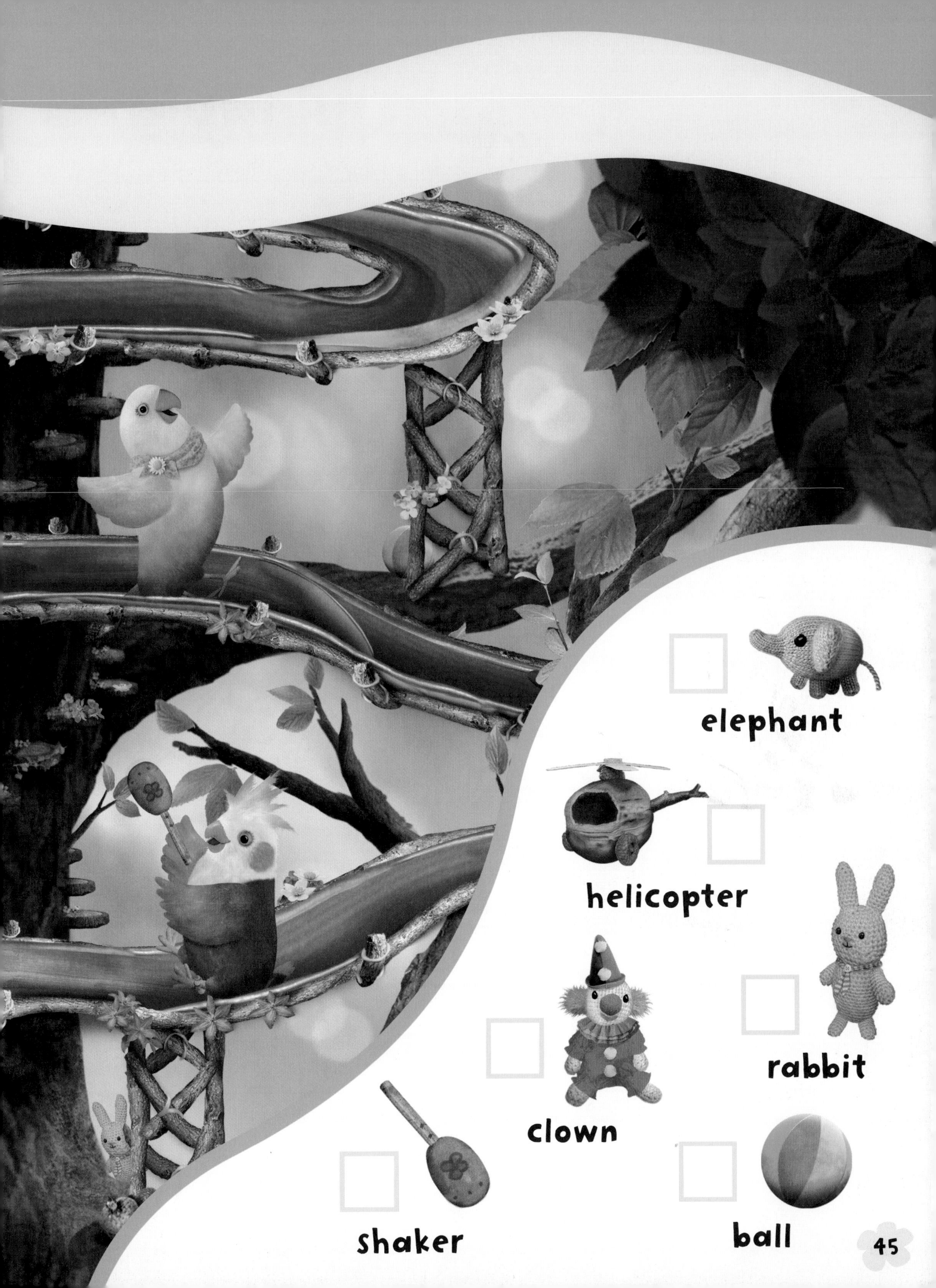
elephant
helicopter
rabbit
clown
shaker
ball

Hello, Quinn!

Draw a picture of Quinn peeping out of the window. Then colour his amazing windmill home.

Mr Beakman is telling stories round the campfire.

Can you spot five differences between the top and bottom pictures?

Answers: Mr B's scarf is purple and he has an extra pink flower on his jacket; a marshmallow is missing; there are some stones missing from around the fire; there is a blue worm peeping out of the tent.

Hide-and-seek

Samuel, Rudy and Muffin are playing hide-and-seek. Just now, it's Samuel's turn to seek.

Can you find Muffin and Rudy? Look around the tree and behind the leaves and flowers!

Rudy

Missy

Mr and Mrs Lovebird and Missy have decided to join in the game. Now, where could they be hiding?

Do you like playing hide-and-seek?

Muffin

A CHORUS FOR US!

1 It was another lovely day on 3rd & Bird. A happy humming sound was coming from Mrs Billingsley's garden. What was she doing? Muffin, Rudy and Samuel hopped along to find out.

2 Mrs Billingsley sang a lovely long note for them. Then she explained proudly that she was in the Bird Chorus - a group of birds who sing together.

3 'We like to sing, too,' said Samuel, and he, Rudy and Muffin all lined up to sing to her.

4 Muffin jumped onto her own branch, shook her bottom and danced and sang very cutely:

Do da Muffin!
Da Muffin!
Shake-a-shake,
Da Muffin!
Uh-uh-oooooh...
Da da da Muffin!

5 Mrs Billingsley thought it was wonderful. 'Wait until you see this,' said Rudy, as she hopped onto her own branch to perform:

Boom-wiki-wiki-wiki-wiki!
Boom-boom-wiki-wiki-wiki-wiki!
Boom-boom-wiki-wiki-boom-
wiki-wiki-boom-boom-boom!
And a wiki-wiki-boom!

6 Mrs Billingsley thought this was charming, too. Rudy encouraged Samuel to have a turn. Samuel hopped onto a branch and sang:

Forget about all the rest,
3rd & Bird's the best.
Yes, 3rd & Bird's the best
branch around!

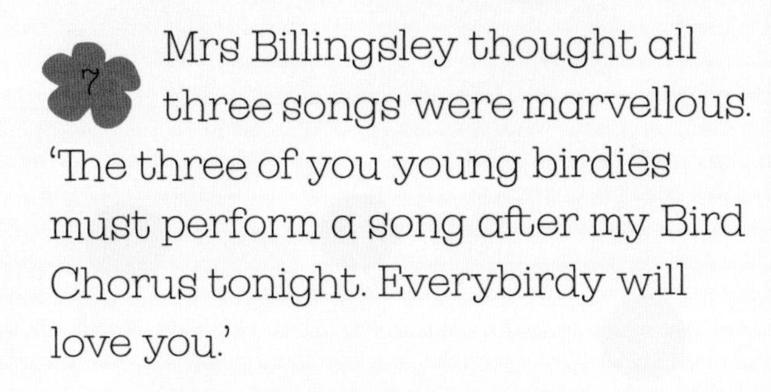

7 Mrs Billingsley thought all three songs were marvellous. 'The three of you young birdies must perform a song after my Bird Chorus tonight. Everybirdy will love you.'

8 Samuel asked if they could sing three songs at the show. But Mrs Billingsley said there was only time for one. 'I must get ready now. See you all later,' she said and went into her house.

9 Rudy and Muffin started to argue about which song it should be. Rudy wanted her song, Wiki-wiki. Muffin wanted her song, Da Muffin.

10 Samuel stepped in to stop them arguing. 'Rudy, Muffin, come on,' he said. 'The show is tonight. We can work something out together.'

11 Samuel had an idea about what to do. 'Let's make one song out of all our songs and do a dance to go with it,' he said. Muffin and Rudy thought this was a great idea.

12 Down at the Bird Theatre the whole town was watching Mrs Billingsley and her chorus perform. They sounded lovely.

13 When they had finished, the audience clapped politely and Mrs Billingsley took a big bow. Muffin, Rudy and Samuel watched from the wings, waiting for their turn.

14 Samuel came on stage first and sang in quite a serious way, like the Bird Chorus. Then he threw off his purple robe and started to dance. The audience loved it.

15 Rudy flew in and hung upside-down from the top of the stage, singing the words of the Wiki-wiki song, and then landed on the stage to do a dance with Muffin. The audience couldn't stop laughing.

16 Finally Samuel, Muffin and Rudy were all on stage together, performing part of the Da Muffin song and part of the Wiki-wiki song, and dancing and whistling. The audience loved them and clapped loudly as the three little birdies took a bow.

Bird Theatre

Draw a picture of someone singing and dancing on the Bird Theatre stage. Then colour it in.

Sky whizz!

Rudy is always busy. She loves to fly around and make patterns in the air.

Come on everybody

Use a pencil to trace over the dotted lines. Can you read what Rudy has written in the sky?

Birdie card

Samuel and Muffin want to make a card for Mr Beakman. Read the picture clue story to find out why.

Samuel and Muffin made a card to thank their teacher Mr. Beakman.

This is the reason why...

Samuel and Muffin wanted to learn a new tune. It was tricky.

Mr. Beakman was very patient. He helped Samuel and Muffin to learn the tune.

Mr. Beakman whistled the tune over and over again.

Samuel and Muffin didn't give up trying. The tune was

Happy Birthday.

Samuel and Muffin learnt the tune. Hooray!

They whistled it to Rudy on her **birthday.**

Samuel

Muffin

Rudy

Mr. Beakman

tune

You will need:

- a rectangular piece of card
- paints, pencils or crayons
- craft materials for decoration
- a grown-up to help you

1. Fold the card in half.

2. Write your greeting on the front of the card in big, bold letters. It might say: 'Thank You' or 'Happy Birthday'.

3. On the inside of the card draw a picture of a friend from 3rd & Bird, and decorate it. Leave some space for the writing.

4. Write your name.

5. Your card is now ready to give to your friend.

Going for a ride

Samuel is pulling
Muffin home after a
long day's play.
Can you help by leading
them along the trail?

My own home

Imagine you lived on 3rd & Bird.
What would your home look like?
It might be a mixture of Samuel and
Rudy's homes. Or you might live in
a home shaped like a fruit,
with windmill sails, too!

Draw a picture of your make-believe home on 3rd & Bird.

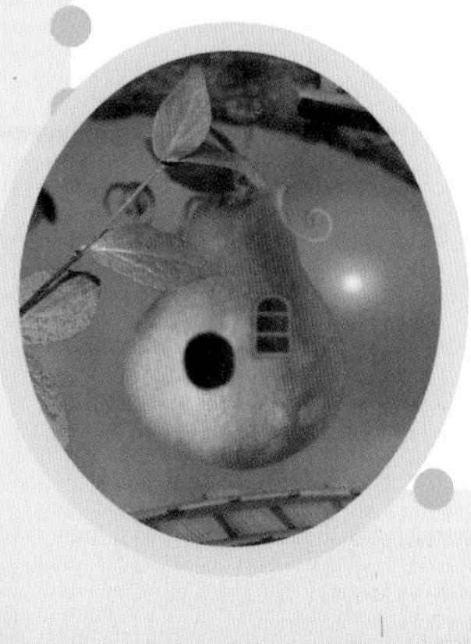

Nature Spotting

As Samuel tidies up, he notices the amazing flowers and plants all around the Lovebird home. Look carefully at these nature shapes. Draw a line using your finger to match each white shape with its coloured picture.

DIY treasure hunt

Samuel, Rudy and Muffin like making their own treasure hunts. It's easy to make a treasure hunt but ask a grown-up to help you at first.

Hide a few toys round your home or in your garden.

Ask someone you know to try and find the toys. If they get stuck, you can help them by saying that they are hot or cold when they are near (hot) or far away (cold) from the toy. For a different kind of treasure hunt you can use pieces of paper with pictures or messages on them.

Did you find the 5 worms and 5 ladybirds hidden in this book?

The five worms were on the following pages:
6, 14, 37, 40, 46

The five ladybirds were on the following pages:
16, 32, 46, 56, 61